TIMELESS SONGS
EASY PIANO

A Collection of 25 Great Standards

Published by
WISE PUBLICATIONS
14-15 Berners Street, London W1T 3LJ,
United Kingdom.

Exclusive Distributors:
MUSIC SALES LIMITED
Distribution Centre,
Newmarket Road, Bury St Edmunds, Suffolk IP33 3YB,
United Kingdom.
MUSIC SALES CORPORATION
180 Madison Avenue, 24th Floor, New York NY 10016,
United States of America.
MUSIC SALES PTY LIMITED
Units 3-4, 17 Willfox Street, Condell Park, NSW 2200,
Australia.

Order No. AM1009943
ISBN 978-1-78305-829-7

Compiled and edited by Jenni Norey.
Music arranged by Alistair Watson.
Music processed by Paul Ewers Music Design.
Cover designed by Michael Bell Design.
Printed in the EU.

Your guarantee of quality
As publishers, we strive to produce every book to the highest commercial standards.
This book has been carefully designed to minimise awkward page turns
and to make playing from it a real pleasure.
Particular care has been given to specifying acid-free, neutral-sized paper made from
pulps which have not been elemental chlorine bleached.
This pulp is from farmed sustainable forests and was produced with special regard for the environment.
Throughout, the printing and binding have been planned to ensure a sturdy,
attractive publication which should give years of enjoyment.
If your copy fails to meet our high standards, please inform us and we will gladly replace it.

www.musicsales.com

TIMELESS SONGS
EASY PIANO

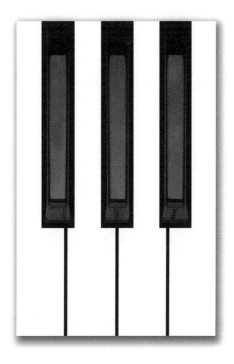

WISE PUBLICATIONS
part of The Music Sales Group

London / New York / Paris / Sydney / Copenhagen / Berlin / Madrid / Hong Kong / Tokyo

An Affair To Remember

Words by Harold Adamson & Leo McCarey
Music by Harry Warren

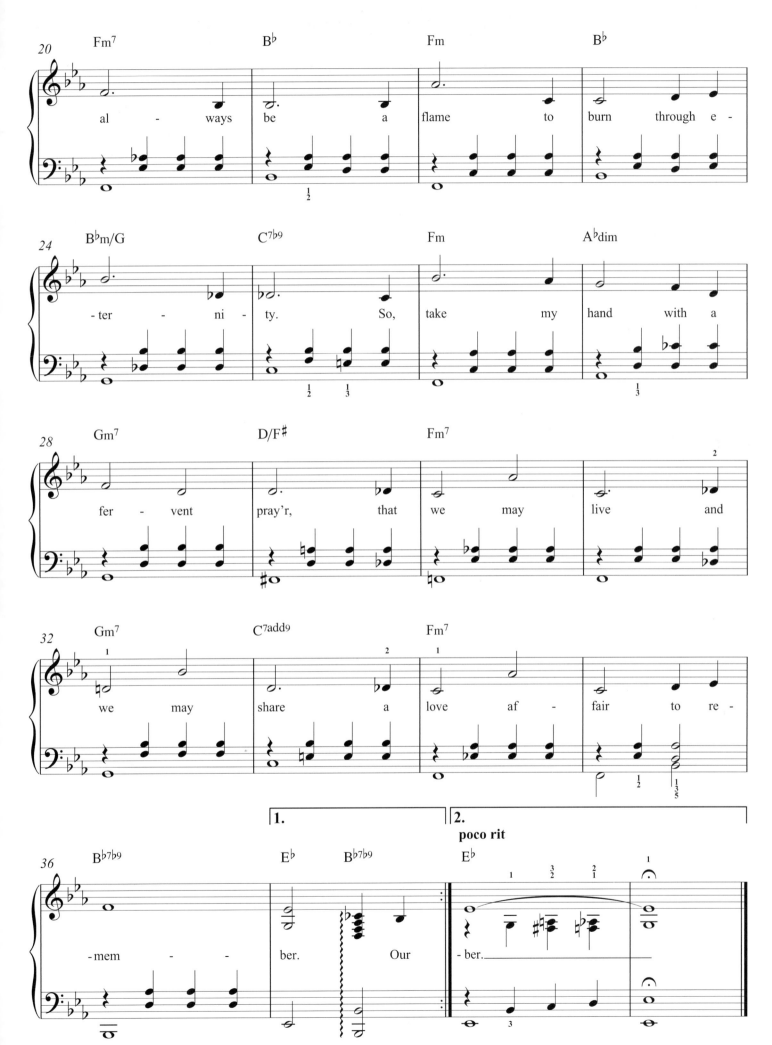

7

April Love

Words by Paul Francis Webster
Music by Sammy Fain

At Last

Words by Mack Gordon
Music by Harry Warren

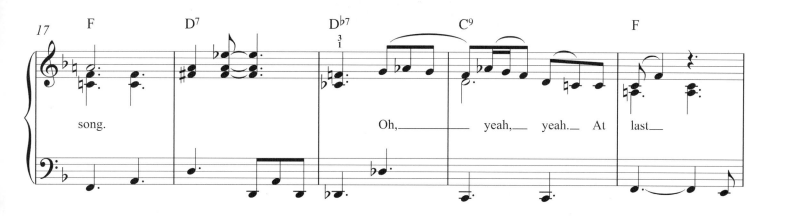

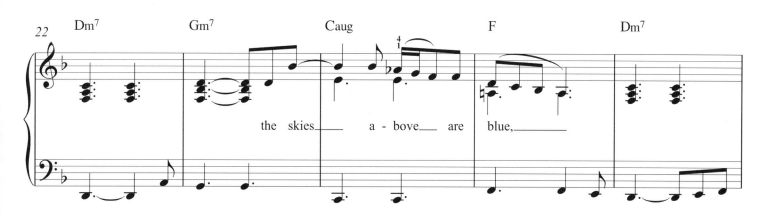

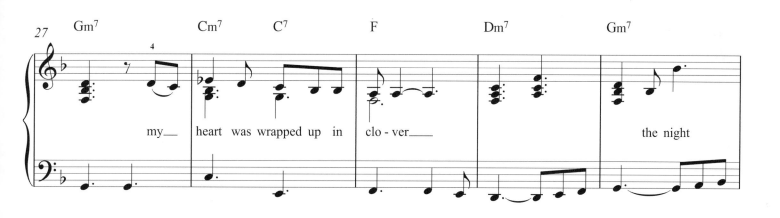

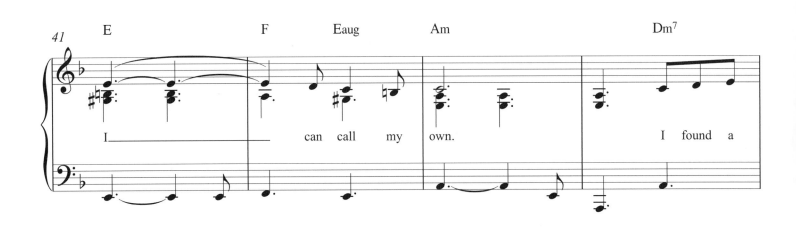

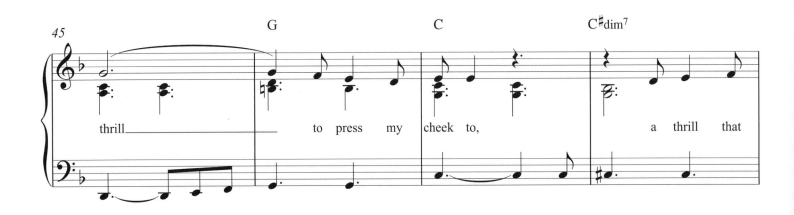

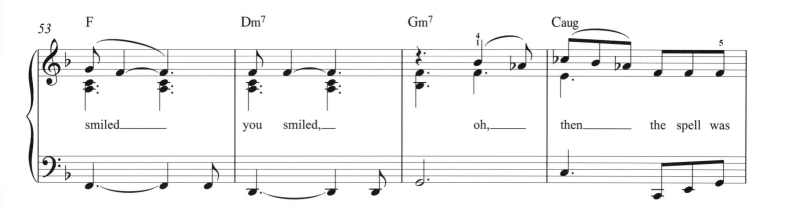

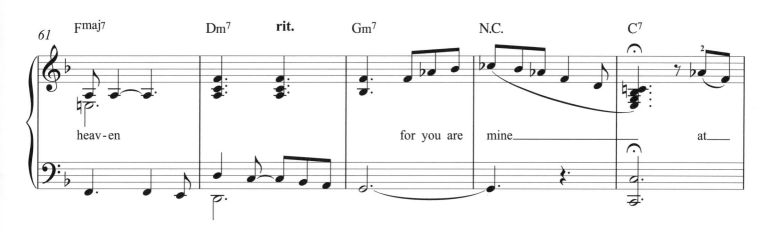

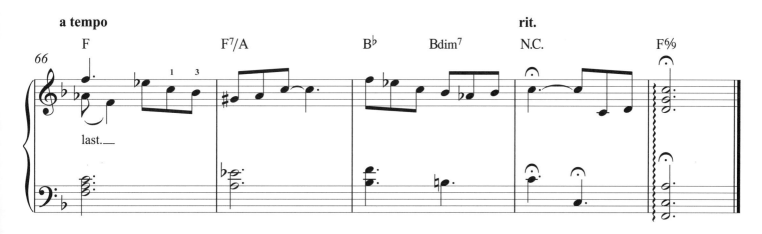

Almost Like Being In Love

Words by Alan Jay Lerner
Music by Frederick Loewe

15

Blue Moon

Words by Lorenz Hart
Music by Richard Rodgers

19

By The Light Of The Silvery Moon

Words & Music by Edward Madden & Gus Edwards

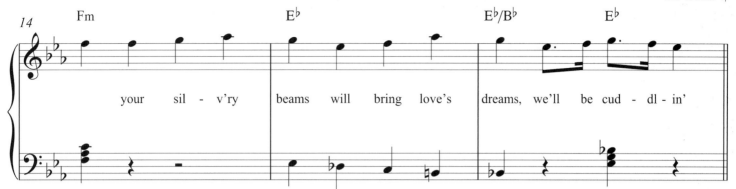

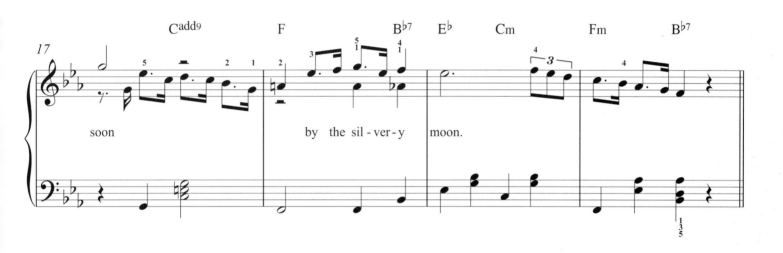

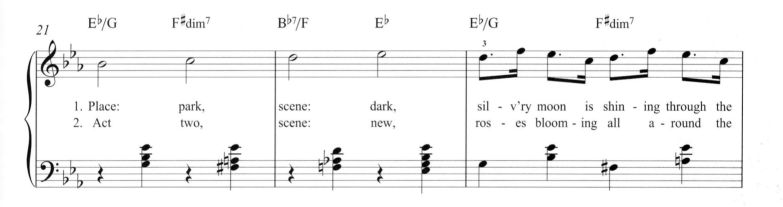

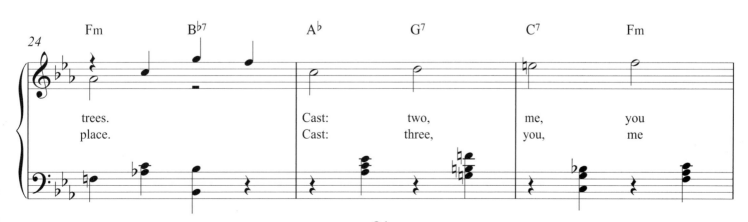

21

sound of kis - ses blow - ing on the breeze. Act one,
preach - er with a sol - emn look - ing face. Choir sings,

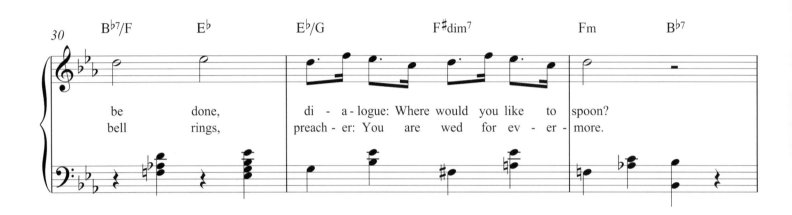

be done, di - a - logue: Where would you like to spoon?
bell rings, preach - er: You are wed for ev - er - more.

D.S. al Coda

My cue: with you un - der-neath the sil - v'ry moon. By the
Act two: all through, ev - 'ry night the same en - core.

Slow

⊕ *Coda*

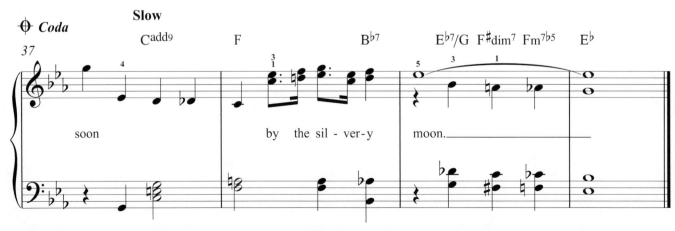

soon by the sil - ver-y moon.

Chattanooga Choo Choo

Words by Mack Gordon
Music by Harry Warren

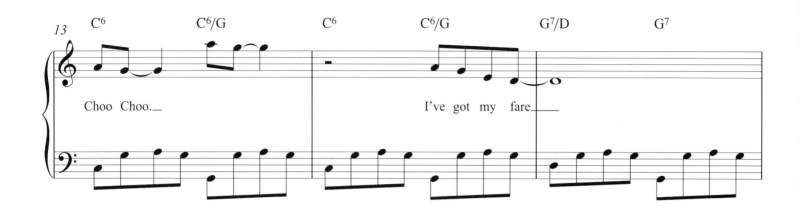

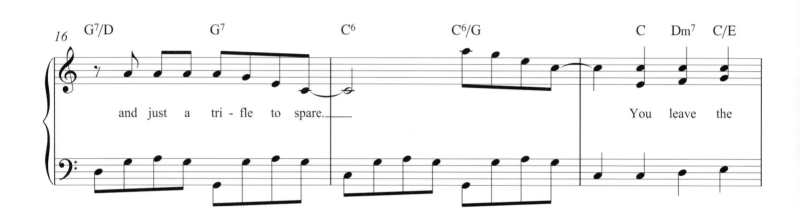

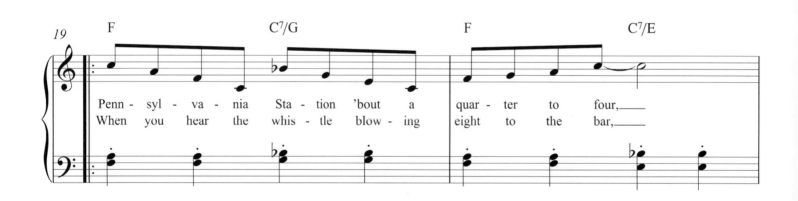

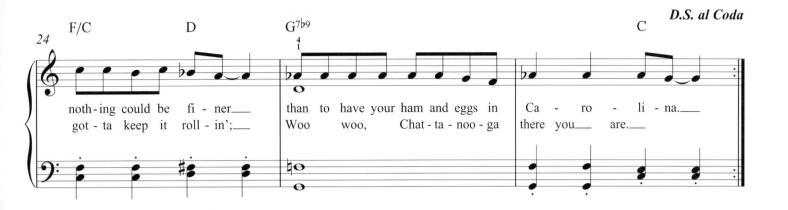

nothing could be fi - ner___
gotta keep it roll - in';___
than to have your ham and eggs in
Woo woo, Chat - ta - noo - ga
Ca - ro - li - na.___
there you___ are.___

⊕ *Coda*

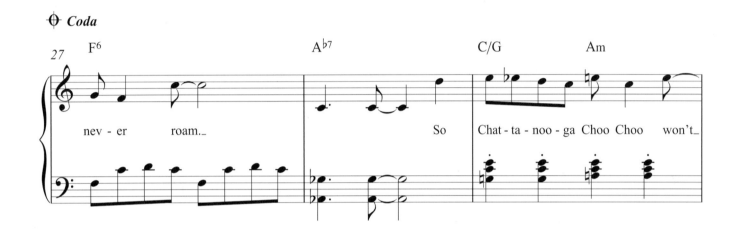

nev - er roam.___
So Chat - ta - noo - ga Choo Choo won't___

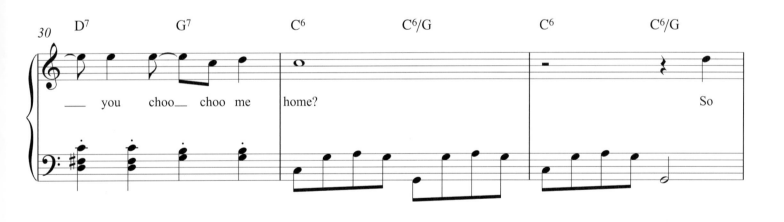

___ you choo___ choo me home?
So

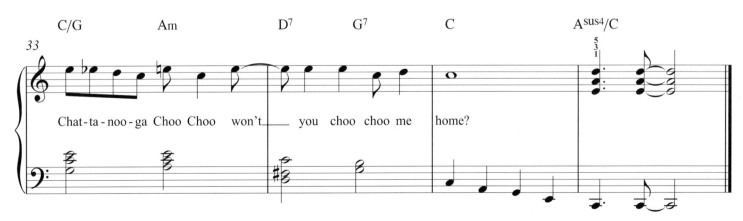

Chat - ta - noo - ga Choo Choo won't___ you choo choo me home?

A Certain Smile

Words by Paul Francis Webster
Music by Sammy Fain

Don't Sit Under The Apple Tree (With Anyone Else But Me)

Words & Music by Sam H. Stept, Lew Brown
& Charles Tobias

How D'ya Like Your Eggs In The Morning?

Words by Sammy Cahn
Music by Nikolaus Brodszky

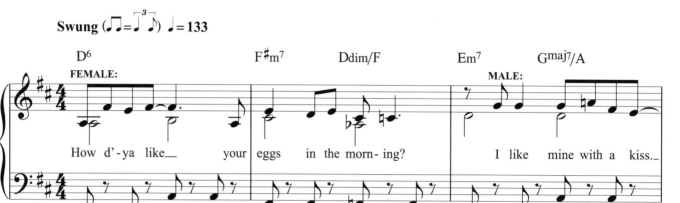

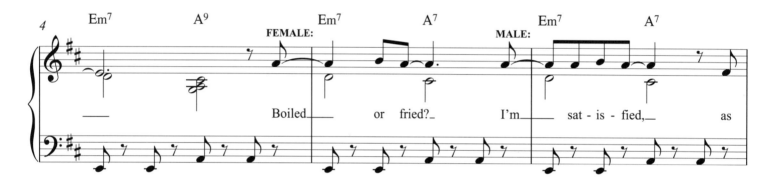

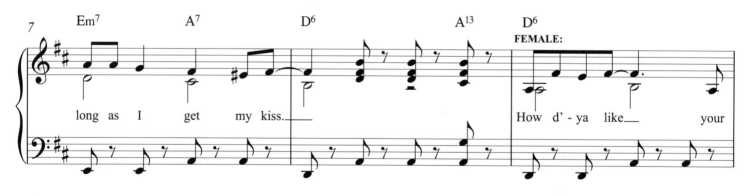

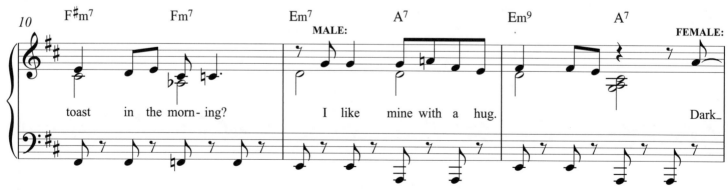

I Fall In Love Too Easily

Words by Sammy Cahn
Music by Jule Styne

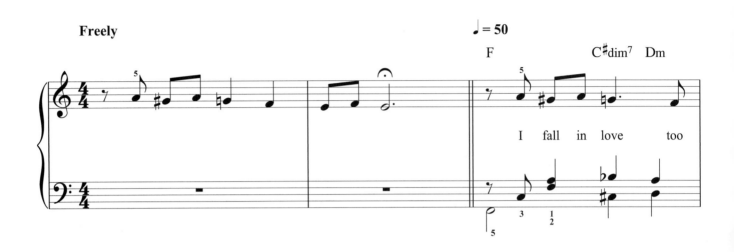

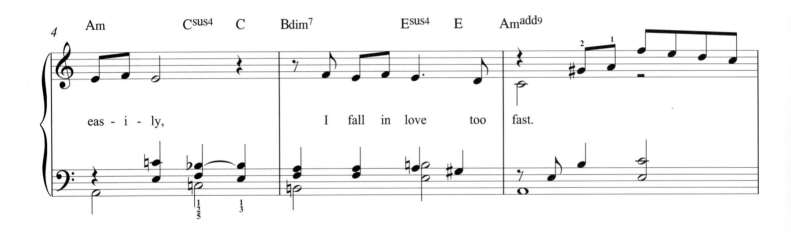

last. My heart should be well schooled 'cause I've been

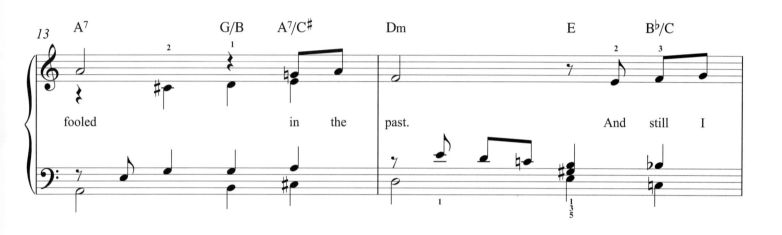

fooled in the past. And still I

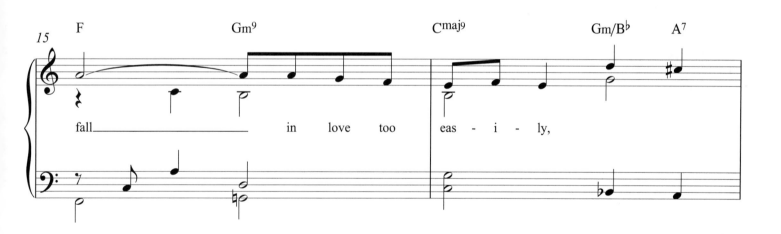

fall_____ in love too eas - i - ly,

poco rit.

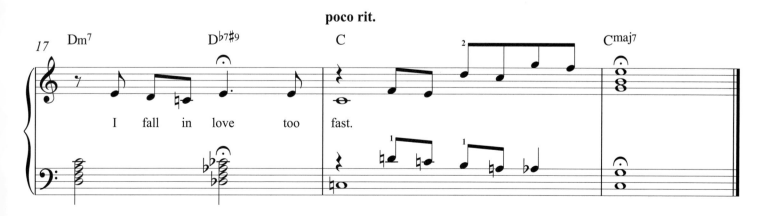

I fall in love too fast.

37

I'm In The Mood For Love

Words & Music by Dorothy Fields & Jimmy McHugh

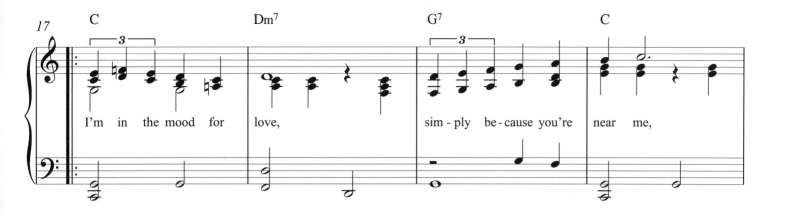

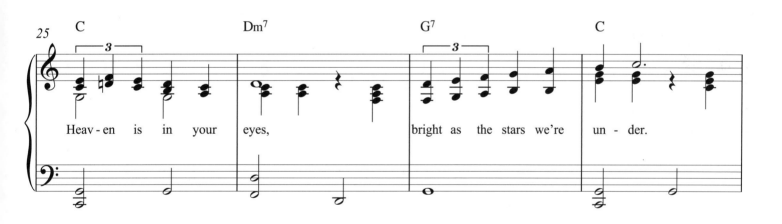

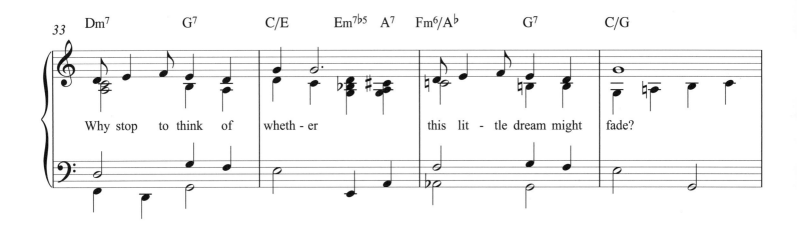

Why stop to think of wheth - er this lit - tle dream might fade?

We've put our hearts to - geth - er, now we are one, I'm not a - fraid!

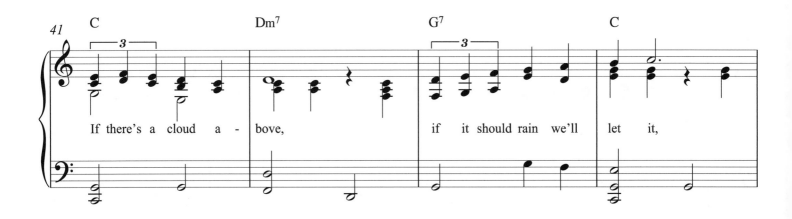

If there's a cloud a - bove, if it should rain we'll let it,

but for to-night, for - get it! I'm in the mood for love.   love.

40

Laura

Words by Johnny Mercer
Music by David Raksin

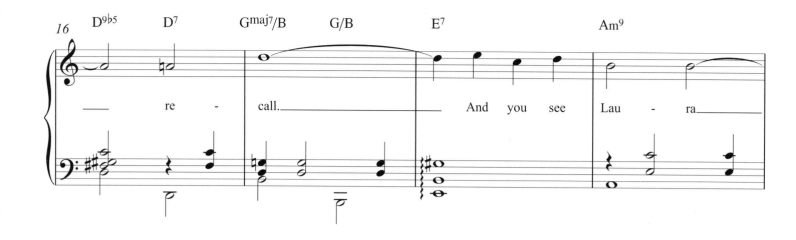

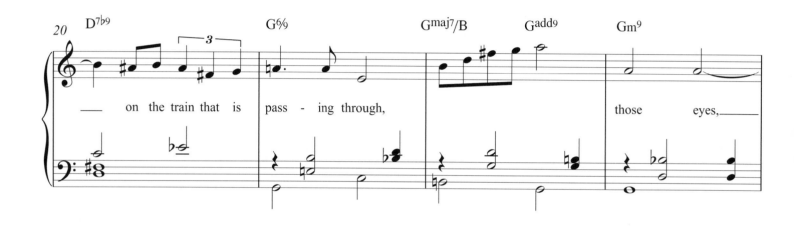

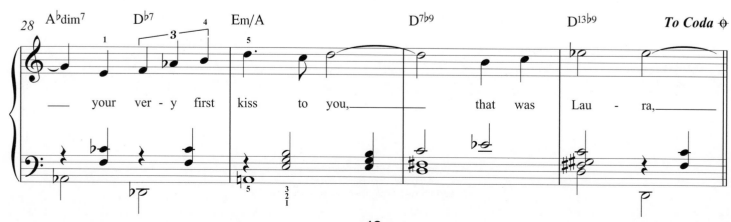

but she's on-ly a dream.

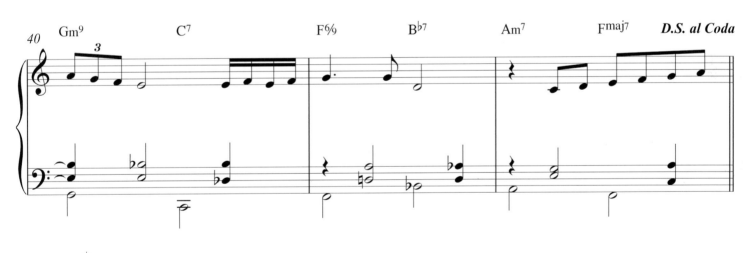

D.S. al Coda

but she's on-ly a dream.

43

Let's Face The Music And Dance

Words & Music by Irving Berlin

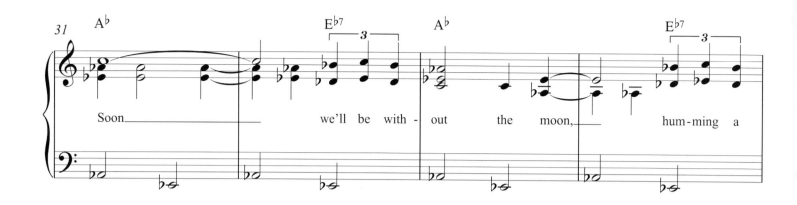

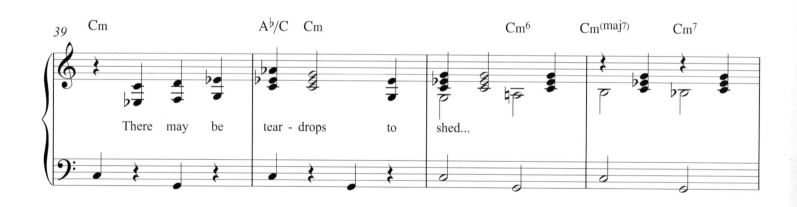

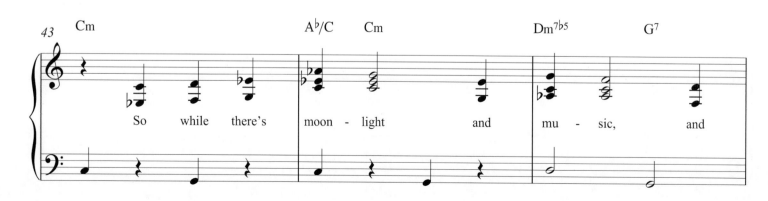

love,   and   ro -   mance...

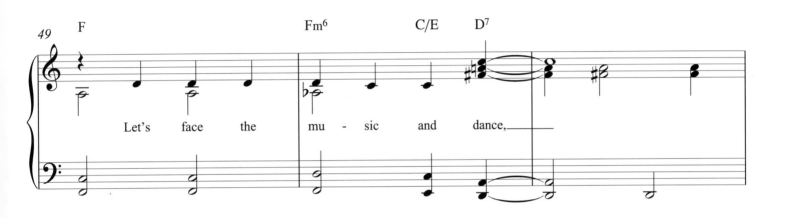

Let's   face   the   mu - sic   and   dance,_____

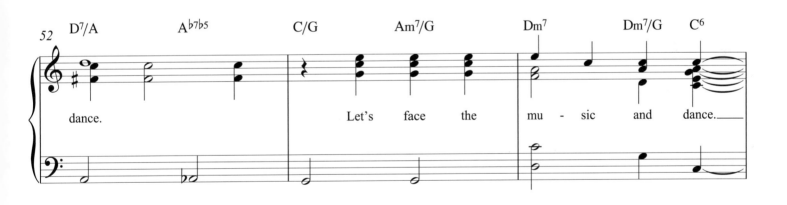

dance.   Let's   face   the   mu - sic   and   dance._____

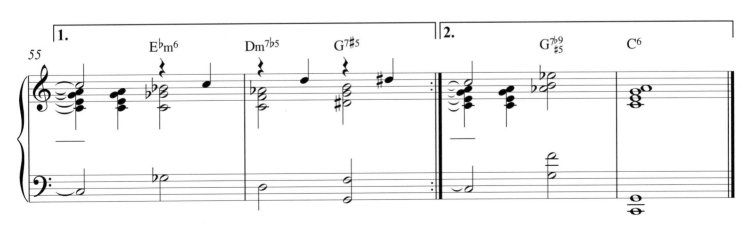

Oops!

Words by Johnny Mercer
Music by Harry Warren

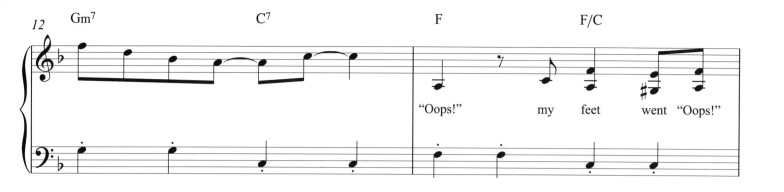

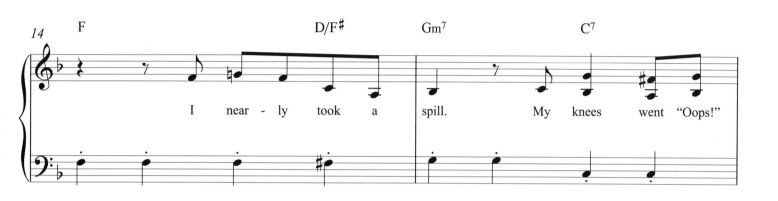

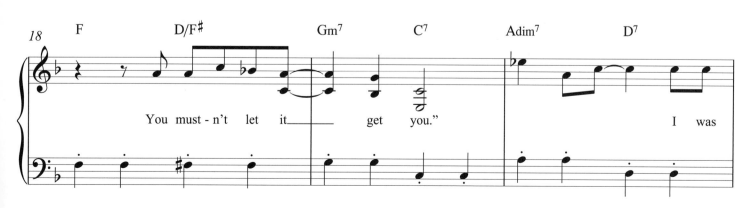

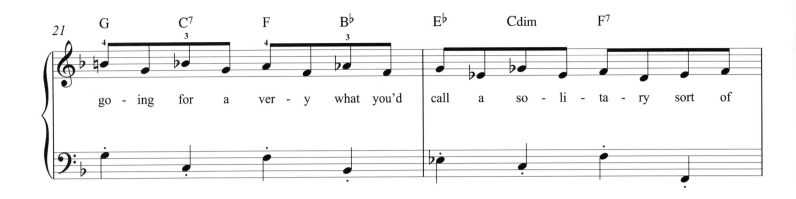

go — ing for a ver — y what you'd call a so — li — ta — ry sort of

stroll; Just a - twid - dl - ing my thumbs when I

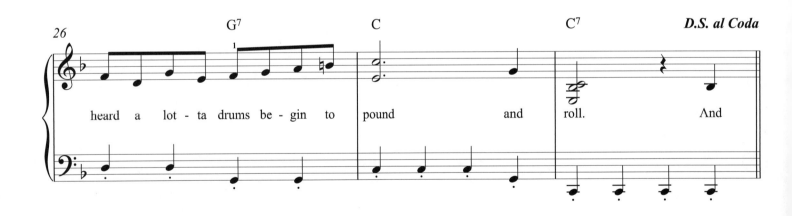

heard a lot - ta drums be - gin to pound and roll. And

D.S. al Coda

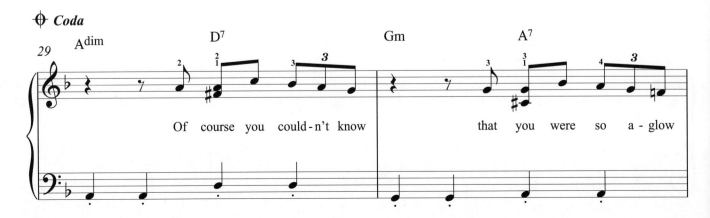

Coda

Of course you could-n't know that you were so a - glow

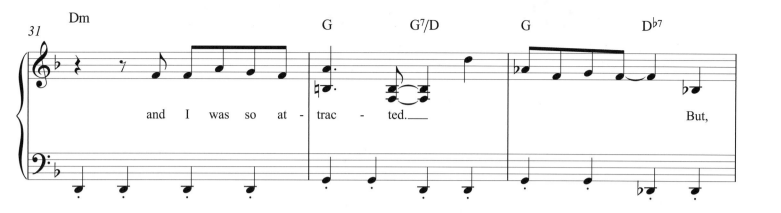

and I was so at - trac - ted.____ But,

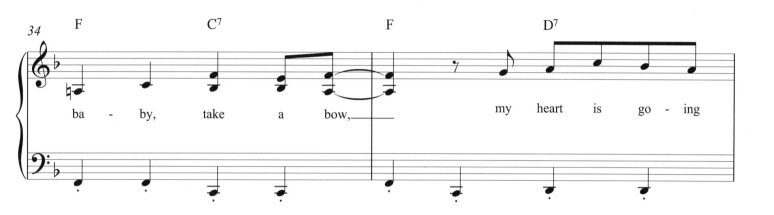

ba - by, take a bow,____ my heart is go - ing

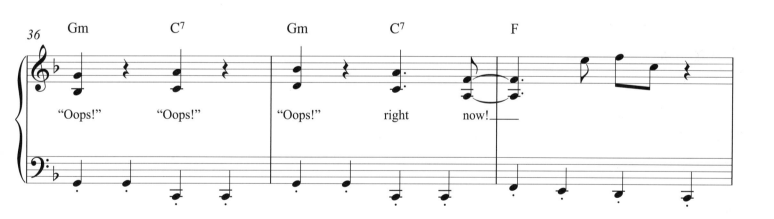

"Oops!" "Oops!" "Oops!" right now!____

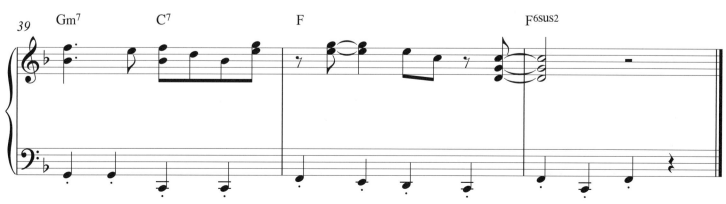

Over The Rainbow

Words by E.Y. Harburg
Music by Harold Arlen

The Shadow Of Your Smile

Words by Paul Francis Webster
Music by Johnny Mandel

Somewhere My Love
(Lara's Theme)

Words by Paul Francis Webster
Music by Maurice Jarre

Three Coins In The Fountain

Words by Sammy Cahn
Music by Jule Styne

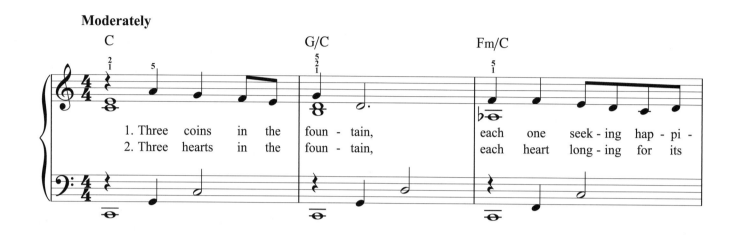

1. Three coins in the foun - tain, each one seek - ing hap - pi -
2. Three hearts in the foun - tain, each heart long - ing for its

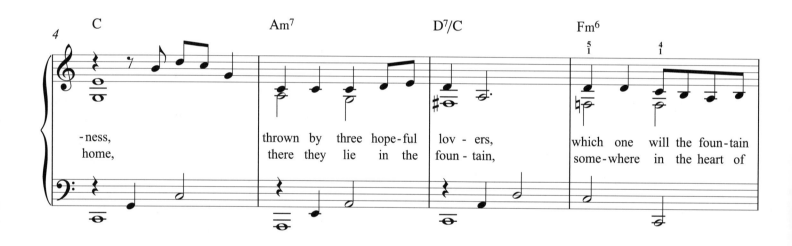

-ness, thrown by three hope - ful lov - ers, which one will the foun-tain
home, there they lie in the foun - tain, some - where in the heart of

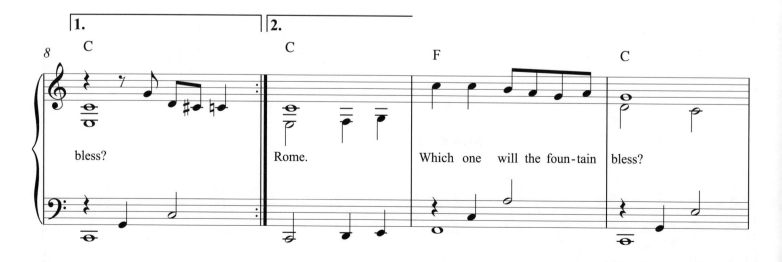

bless? | Rome. Which one will the foun - tain bless?

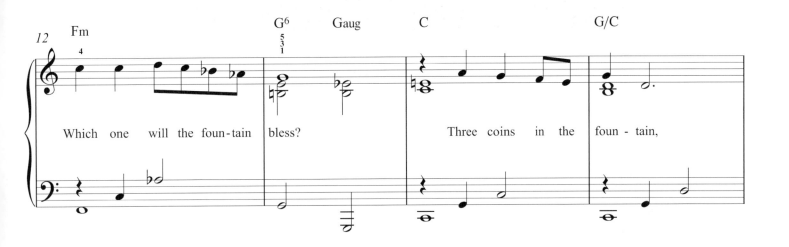

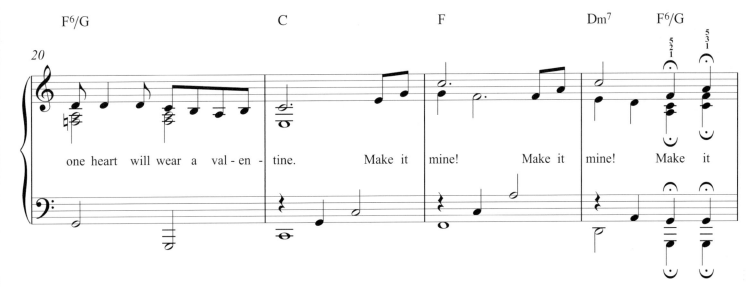

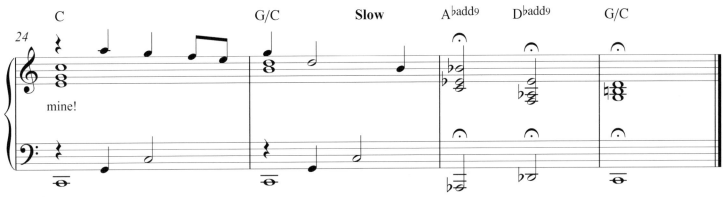

59

Time On My Hands

Words & Music by Vincent Youmans, Harold Adamson
& Mack Gordon

The Trolley Song

Words by Hugh Martin
Music by Ralph Blane

Volare

Words by Francesco Migliacci, Domenico Modugno & Mitchell Parish
Music by Domenico Modugno
Original Italian Text by Domenico Modugno and Francesco Migliacci

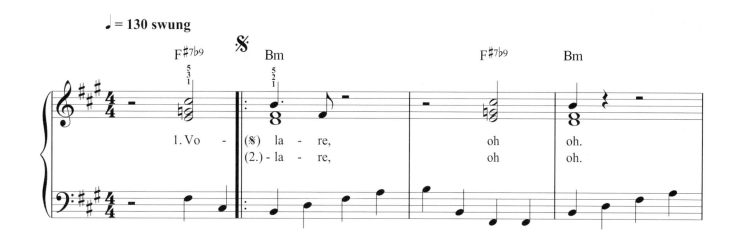

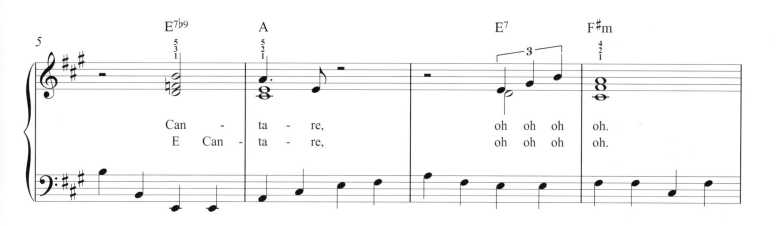

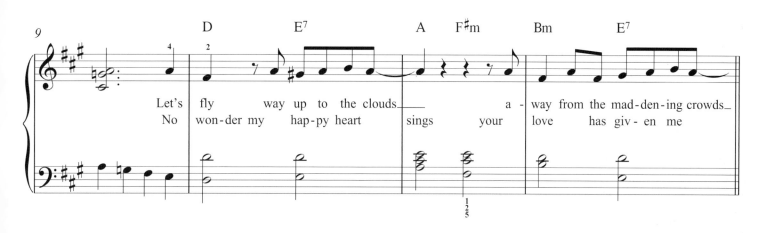

Straight rhythm

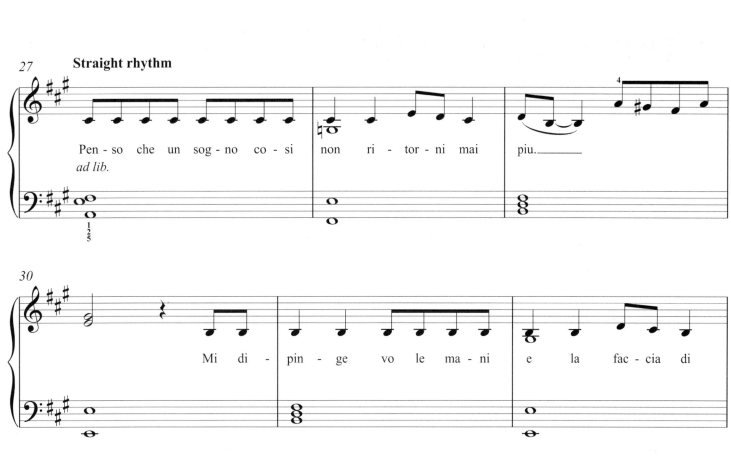

Pen - so che un sog - no co - si non ri - tor - ni mai piu._____

ad lib.

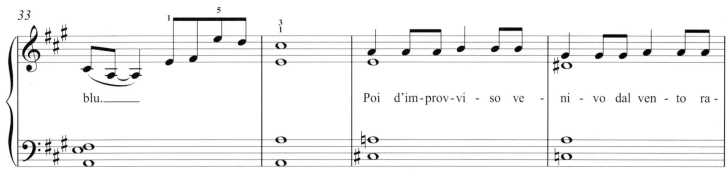

Mi di - pin - ge vo le ma - ni e la fac - cia di

blu._____ Poi d'im - prov - vi - so ve - ni - vo dal ven - to ra -

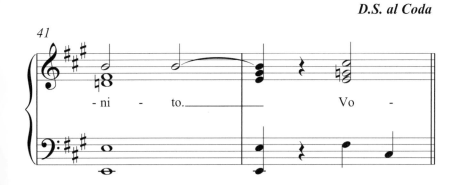

- pi - to.___ E in - co - min - cia - vo a vo - la - re nel cie - lo in - fi -

D.S. al Coda $\oplus$ ***Coda***

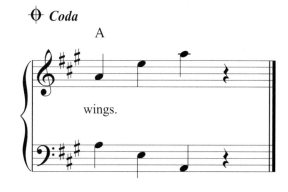

- ni - to._____ Vo -   wings.

Where Do You Go To (My Lovely)

Words & Music by Peter Sarstedt

72

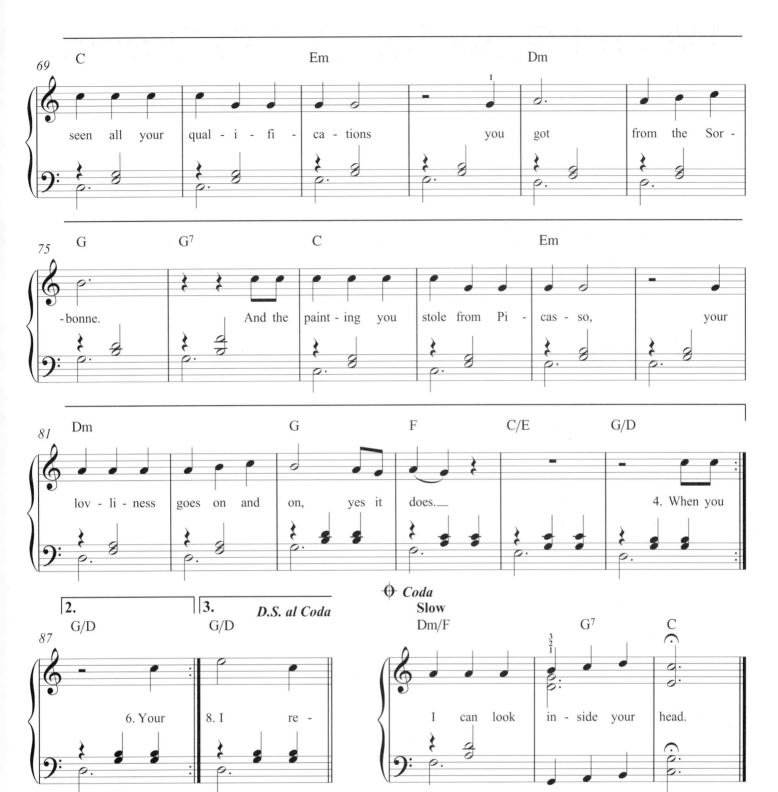

Verse 4:
When you go on your summer vacation
You go to Juan le Pines.
With your carefully designed topless swimsuit
You get an even suntan, on your back and on your legs.

Verse 5:
When the snow falls you're found in St. Moritz
With the others of the jet-set.
And you sip your Napoleon Brandy
But you never get your lips wet, no you don't.

Verse 6:
Your name is heard in high places
You know the Aga Khan.
He sent you a racehorse for Christmas
And you keep it just for fun, for a laugh, ha ha ha.

Verse 7:
They say that when you get married
It'll be to a millionaire.
But they don't realize where you came from
And I wonder if they really care, or give a damn.

Verse 8:
I remember the back streets of Naples
Two children begging in rags.
Both touched with a burning ambition
To shake off their lowly born tags, they try.

Verse 9:
So look into my face Marie-Claire
And remember just who you are.
Then go and forget me forever
But I know you still bear the scar, deep inside, yes you do.

When I Grow Too Old To Dream

Words by Oscar Hammerstein II
Music by Sigmund Romberg

The Windmills Of Your Mind

Words by Alan & Marilyn Bergman
Music by Michel Legrand

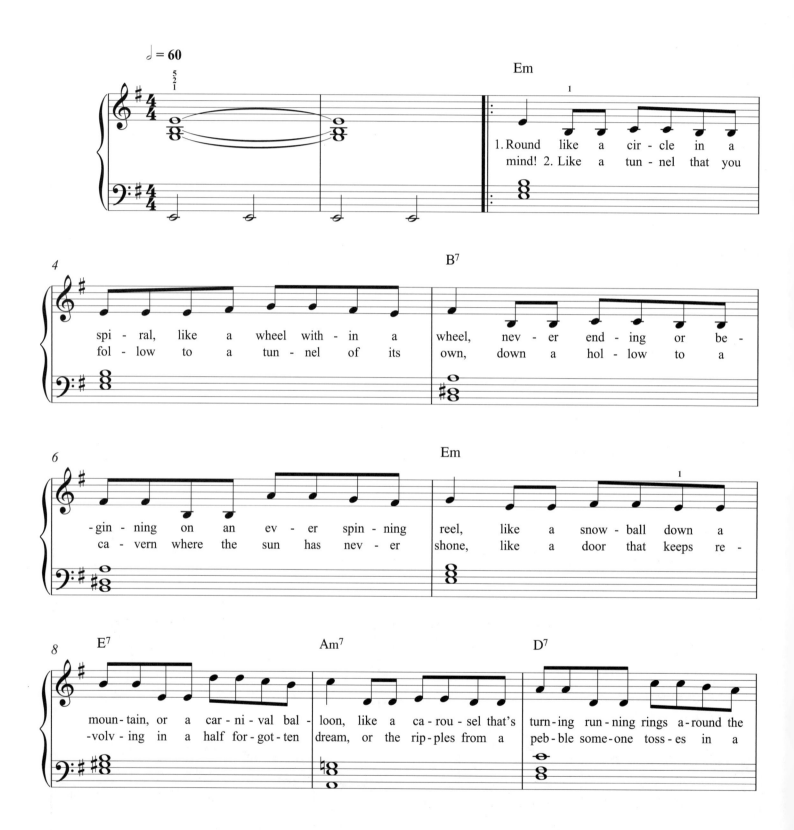

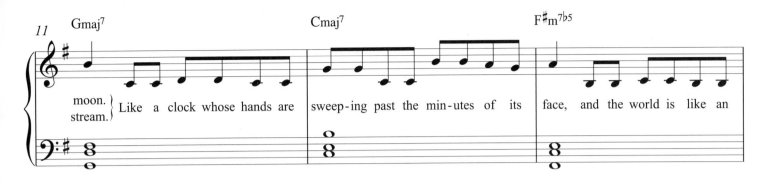

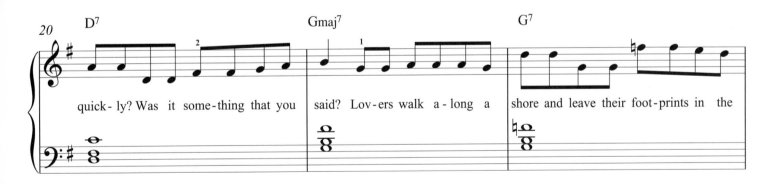

26 E⁷ · · · · · · · · Am · · · · · · · · D⁷ · · · · · · · ·
hall-way and the frag-ment of a song. Half re-mem-bered names and fac-es but to whom do they be-

29 Gmaj7 · · · · · · · · Cmaj7 · · · · · · · · F♯m7♭5 · · · · · · · ·
-long? When you knew that it was o-ver you were sud-den-ly a-ware, that the au-tumn leaves were

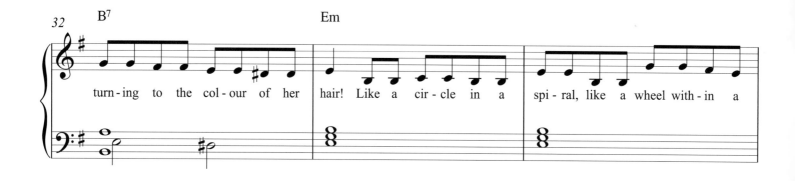

32 B⁷ · · · · · · · · Em · · · · · · · · · · · · · · · ·
turn-ing to the col-our of her hair! Like a cir-cle in a spi-ral, like a wheel with-in a

35 B⁷ · · · · · · · · · · · · · · · · A♯dim · · · · · · · ·
wheel, nev-er end-ing or be-gin-ning on an ev-er spin-ning reel, as the i-ma-ges un-

Slow

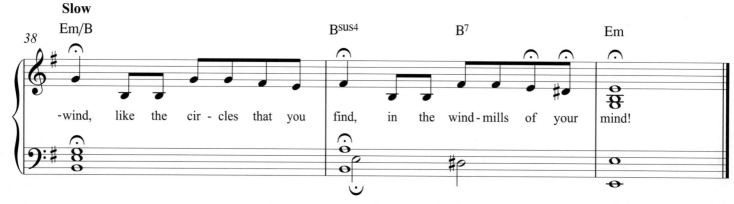

38 Em/B · · · · · · · · Bsus4 · · · · B⁷ · · · · Em
-wind, like the cir-cles that you find, in the wind-mills of your mind!

123456789